# THE ART OF MINDFULNESS

# HAPPY AND ENERGIZED COLOURING

Michael O'Mara Books Limited

First published in Great Britain in 2015 by
Michael O'Mara Books Limited
9 Lion Yard
Tremadoc Road
London SW4 7NQ

A CIP catalogue record for this book is available from the British Library.

Papers used by Michael O'Mara Books Limited are natural, recyclable products
made from wood grown in sustainable forests. The manufacturing processes
conform to the environmental regulations of the country of origin.

ISBN: 978-1-78243-502-0

1 2 3 4 5 6 7 8 9 10

www.mombooks.com

Designed by Ana Bjezancevic and Claire Cater

Illustrations by Amanda Hillier, Angelika Scundamore, Anna Shuttlewood,
Claire Cater, Faye Buckingham, Jo Taylor, Julie Ingram, Katrin Alt,
Louise Wright, Pimlada Phuapradit and Sam Loman

Cover illustration by Pimlada Phuapradit

Printed and bound by L.E.G.O., Viale dell'Industria 2, 36100, Vicenza, Italy

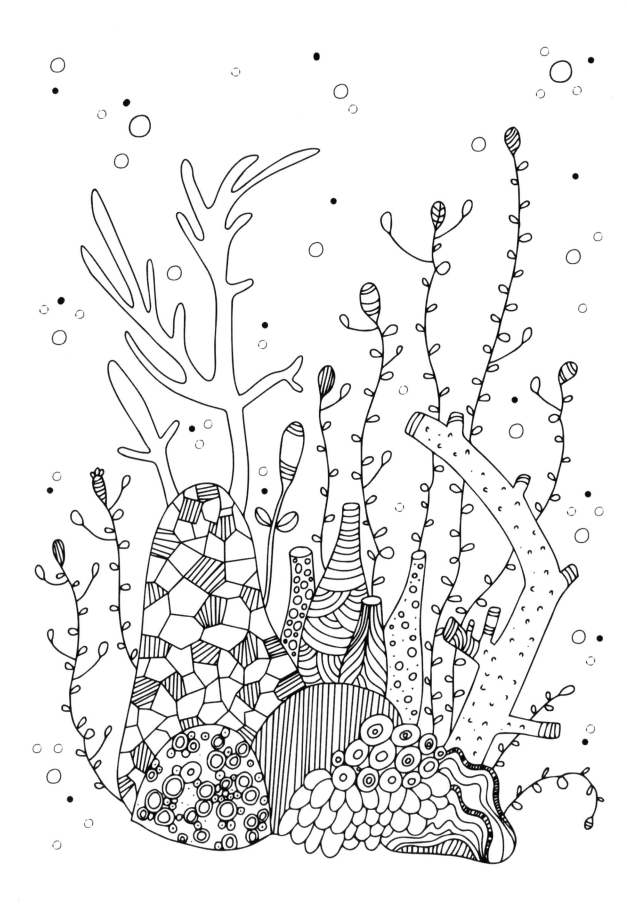

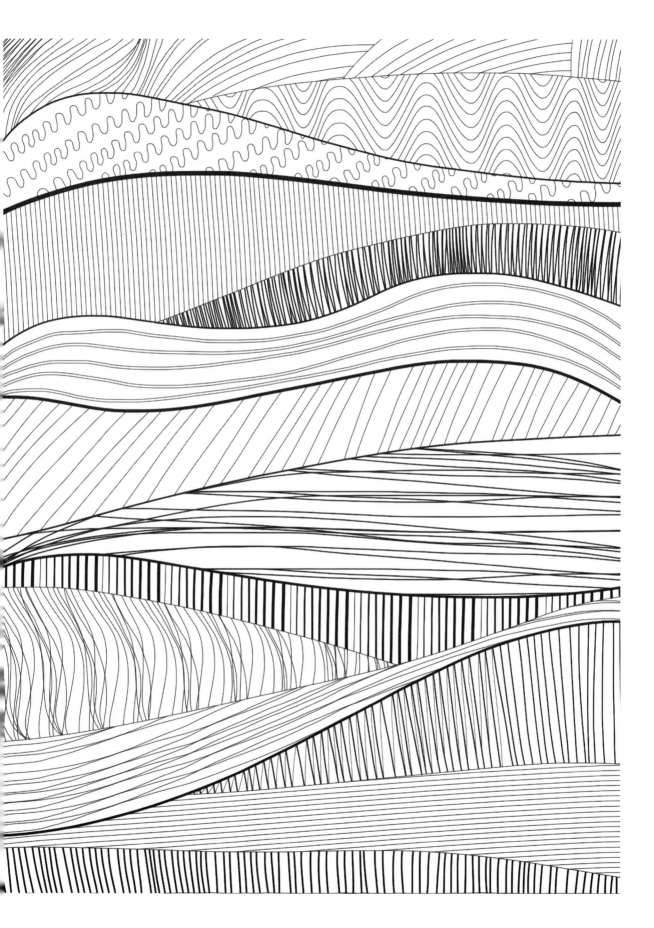